# THE LONESOME ROAD

Words by Gene Austin
Music by Nathaniel Shilkret

**Suggested registration:** saxophone

**Rhythm:** swing

**Tempo:** fairly fast ( ♩ = 132 )

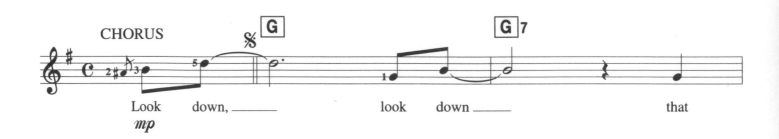

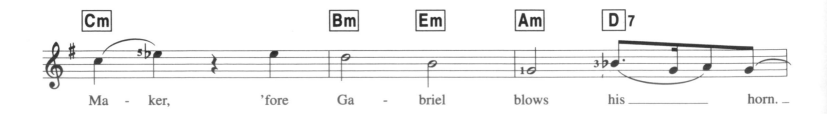

Arranged for portable keyboards *by Kenneth Baker.*

# THE COMPLETE KEYBOARD PLAYER
## DINNER JAZZ

**Wise Publications**
London/New York/Paris/Sydney/Copenhagen/Madrid

Exclusive Distributors:
**Music Sales Limited**
8/9 Frith Street, London W1V 5TZ, England.
**Music Sales Pty Limited**
120 Rothschild Avenue, Rosebery, NSW 2018, Australia.

This book © Copyright 1997 by
Wise Publications
Order No. AM936980
ISBN 0-7119-5746-0

Compiled by Peter Evans
Music arranged by Kenneth Baker
Music processed by MSS Studios

Cover design by Studio Twenty, London

**Your Guarantee of Quality**
As publishers, we strive to produce every book
to the highest commercial standards.
The music has been freshly engraved and the book has been
carefully designed to minimise awkward page turns and to make
playing from it a real pleasure.
Particular care has been given to specifying acid-free, neutral-sized paper
made from pulps which have not been elemental chlorine bleached.
This pulp is from farmed sustainable forests and was produced with special
regard for the environment. Throughout, the printing and binding have been
planned to ensure a sturdy, attractive publication which should give years of enjoyment.
If your copy fails to meet our high standards, please inform us and
we will gladly replace it.

Music Sales' complete catalogue describes thousands of titles and is available in
full colour sections by subject, direct from Music Sales Limited.
Please state your areas of interest and send a cheque/postal order for £1.50 for postage to:
Music Sales Limited, Newmarket Road, Bury St. Edmunds, Suffolk IP33 3YB.

Visit the Internet Music Shop at
http://www.musicsales.co.uk

Printed in Great Britain by
Printwise (Haverhill) Limited, Haverhill, Suffolk.

## IMPROVISATION
(rhythm starts)

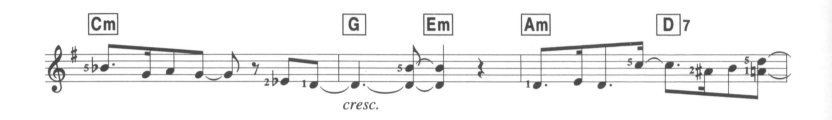

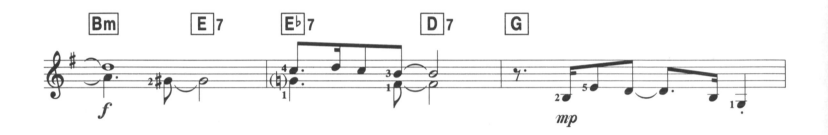

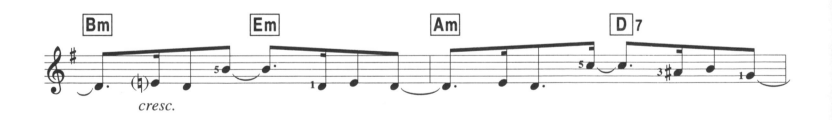

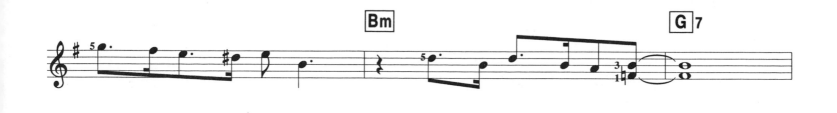

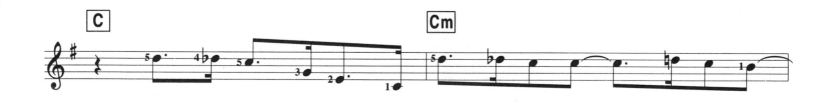

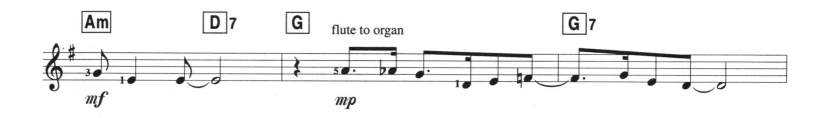

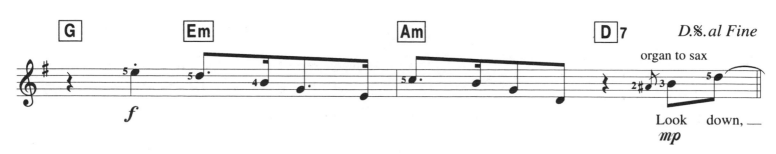

# ONCE IN A WHILE

Words & Music by William H. Butter

**Suggested registration:** clarinet
**Rhythm:** swing
**Tempo:** medium ( ♩ = 100 )

CHORUS

Once in a while _____ will you try to give one ____ lit- tle thought _ to me? _
*mp*

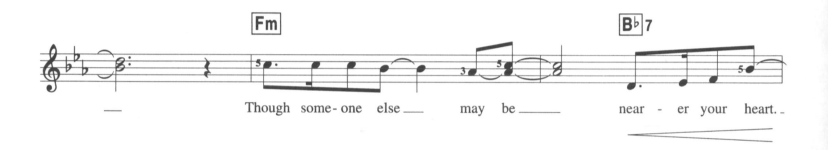

_ Though some-one else ____ may be ____ near - er your heart. _

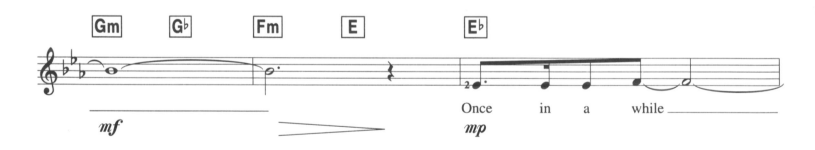

*mf* Once in a while _____
*mp*

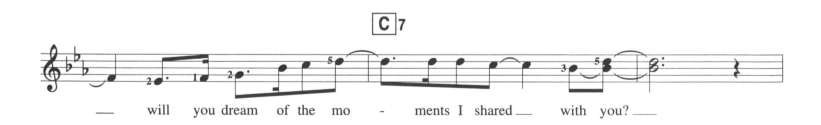

_ will you dream of the mo - ments I shared _ with you? _

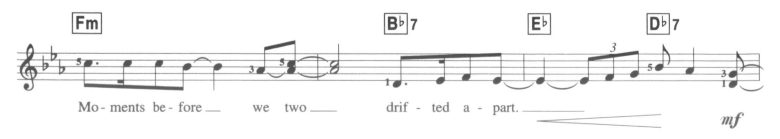

Mo- ments be - fore _ we two ____ drif - ted a - part. _
*mf*

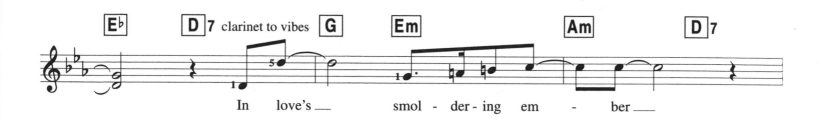

In love's ___ smol - der - ing em - ber ___

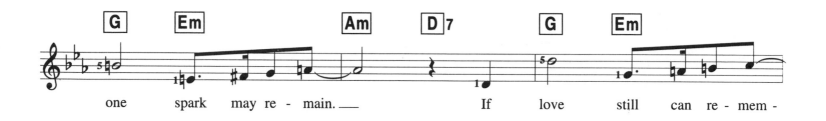

one spark may re - main. ___ If love still can re - mem -

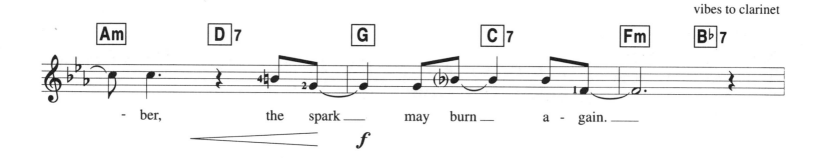

- ber, the spark ___ may burn ___ a - gain. ___

*f*

I know that I'll _____ be con - ten - ted with yes - ter - day's me - mo - ry, ___

*mp*

___ know - ing you think ___ of me ___ once in a while. ___

*cresc.*

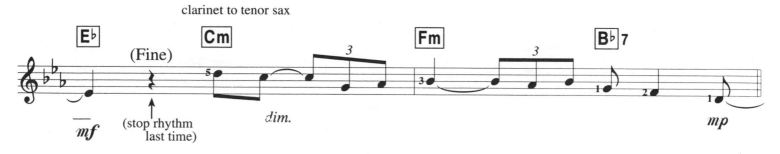

*mf*
(stop rhythm
last time)

*dim.*

*mp*

IMPROVISATION

sax to guitar

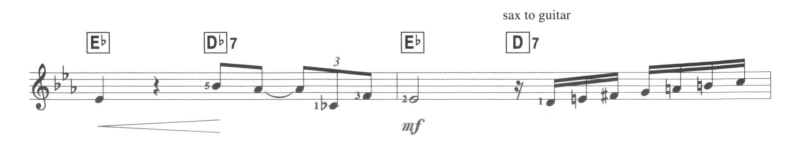

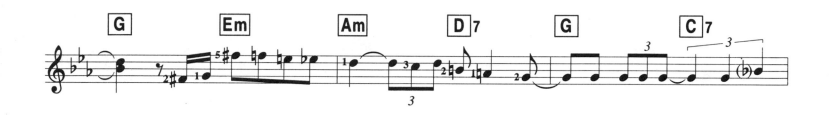

guitar to sax

slip from black note to white

*mp*

sax to clarinet

*D.C. al Fine*

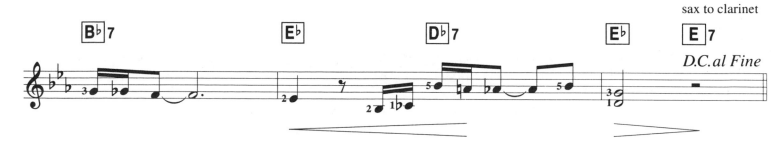

11

# LAZY RIVER

## Words & Music by Hoagy Carmichael & Sidney Arodin

**Suggested registration:** brass ensemble

**Rhythm:** swing

**Tempo:** medium ( ♩ = 116 )

INTRO

CHORUS

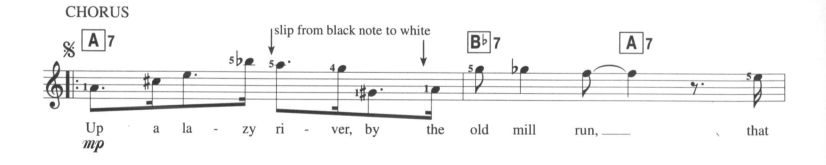

slip from black note to white

Up a la - zy ri - ver, by the old mill run, _____ that

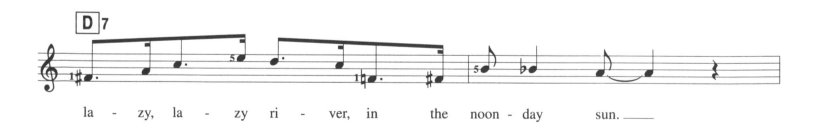

la - zy, la - zy ri - ver, in the noon - day sun. _____

Lin - ger in the shade of a kind old tree, _____

throw a - way your trou - bles, dream a dream ____ with me. ____

*f*

Up a la - zy ri - ver, where the ro - bin's song ____ a -

*mp*

add trombone

wakes a bright new mor - ning, we can loaf a - long. ____ Blue skies up a - bove,

*f*

ev - 'ry - one's in love, up a la - zy ri - ver, ____ how

1.

cut trombone

hap - py you can be, up a la - zy ri - ver ____ with me.

3

2.3.

(Fine)

me, ____ up a la - zy ri - ver ____ with me.

*ff*

(stop rhythm last time)

## IMPROVISATION

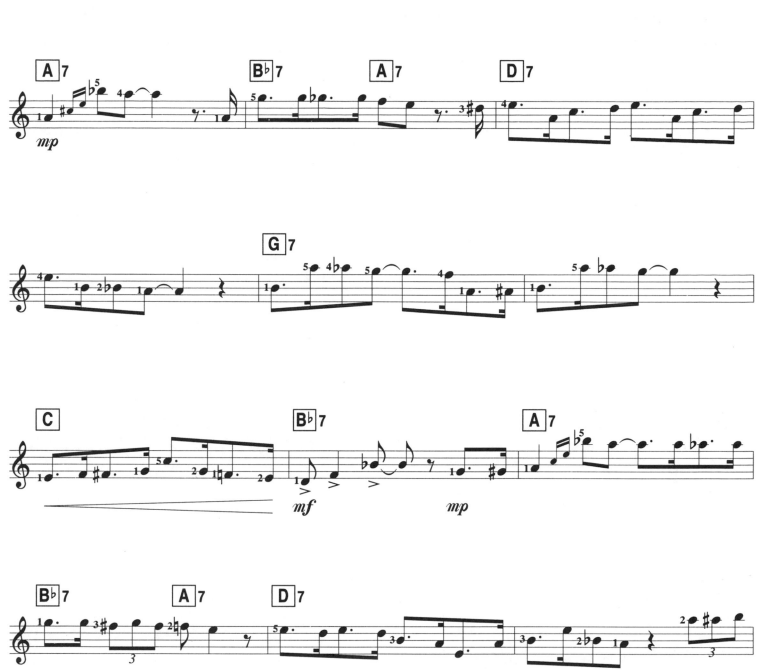

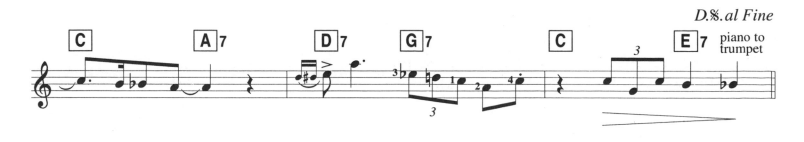

# MISTY

Music by Erroll Garner
Words by Johnny Burke

**Suggested registration:** piano
**Rhythm:** swing
**Tempo:** slow ( ♩ = 72 )

CHORUS

Look at me, I'm as help-less as a kit-ten up a
*mp*

tree, and I feel like I'm cling-ing to a cloud, I can't ___ un-der-stand, ___ I get

mis-ty just hold-ing your hand. ___ Walk my
*mf*          *mp*

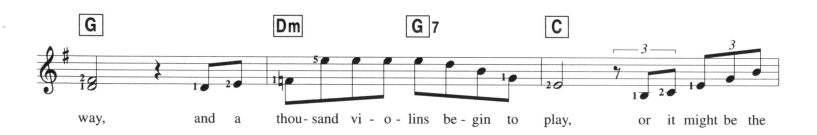

way, and a thou-sand vi-o-lins be-gin to play, or it might be the

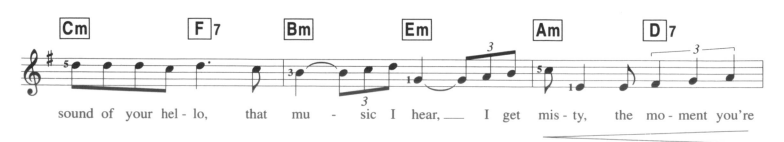

sound of your hel-lo, that mu-sic I hear, ___ I get mis-ty, the mo-ment you're

IMPROVISATION

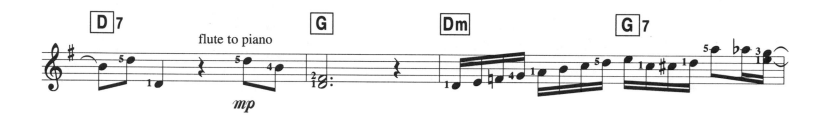

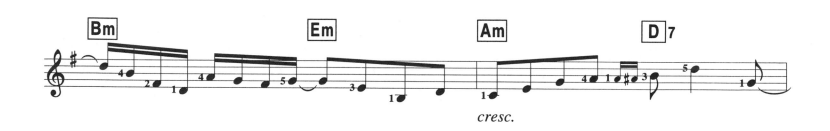

D.%.al Fine

Look at

# LULLABY OF BIRDLAND

Music by George Shearing
Words by George David Weiss

**Suggested registration:** vibraphone

**Rhythm:** swing

**Tempo:** medium ( ♩ = 96 )

CHORUS

Lul - la - by of Bird - land, that's what I al - ways hear
*mp*         *cresc.*

when you sigh. Ne - ver in my word - land could there be ways to re - veal,
*mf*

in a phrase, how I feel. Have you e - ver heard two
*dim.*        *mp*

tur - tle doves bill and coo when they love?
*cresc.*

That's the kind of ma - gic mu - sic we make with our lips when we kiss.
*mf*                                              *f*

And there's a weep-y old wil - low, —
*mp*

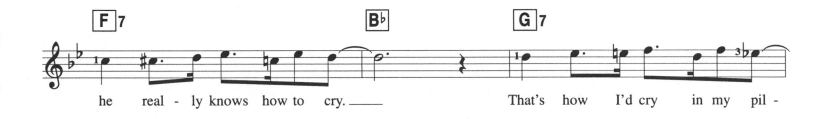

he real - ly knows how to cry. —— That's how I'd cry in my pil -

- low, — if you should tell me fare - well —— and good - bye. —
*cresc.* *mf*

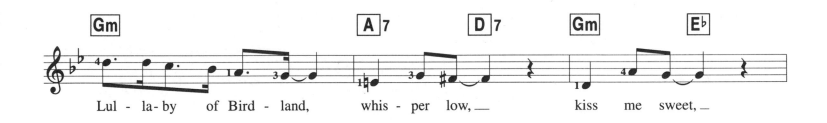

Lul - la- by of Bird - land, whis - per low, — kiss me sweet, —

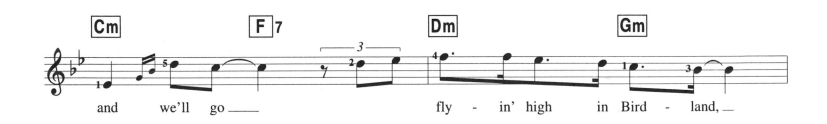

and we'll go —— fly - in' high in Bird - land, —

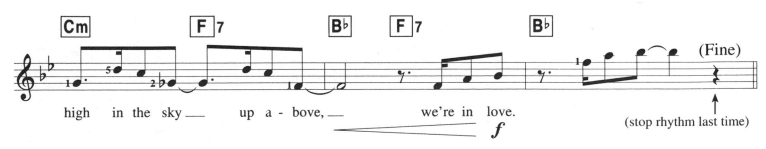

high in the sky — up a - bove, — we're in love.
*f*
(stop rhythm last time)

# IMPROVISATION

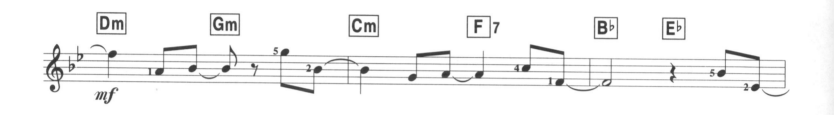

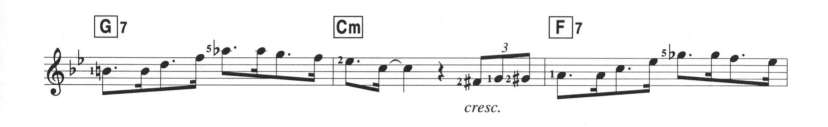

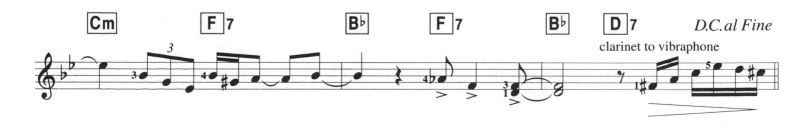

# DON'T DREAM OF ANYBODY BUT ME (LI'L DARLIN')

Words by Bart Howard
Music by Neal Hefti

**Suggested registration:** muted brass

**Rhythm:** swing

**Tempo:** fairly slow ( ♩ = 80 )

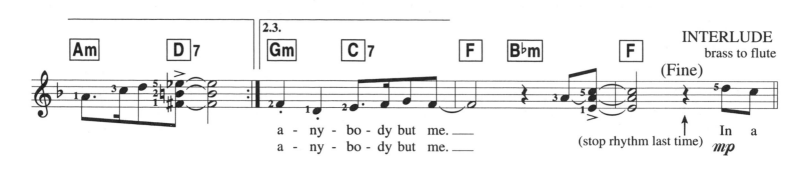

a - ny - bo - dy but me.\_\_\_
a - ny - bo - dy but me.\_\_\_

(stop rhythm last time)  *mp*

In a

ca - fé on the Rhine, _____ a - ny place a - long the line. _____ I'll for -

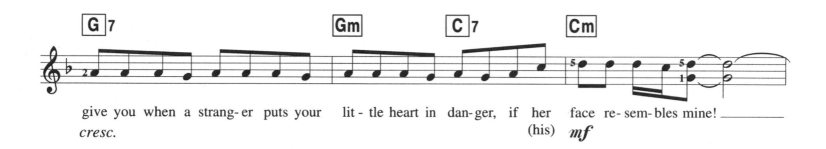

give you when a strang-er puts your lit - tle heart in dan-ger, if her face re-sem-bles mine! _____

*cresc.* (his) *mf*

\_\_\_ When you vi - sit a night-club in 'Fris - co, and the

*mp*

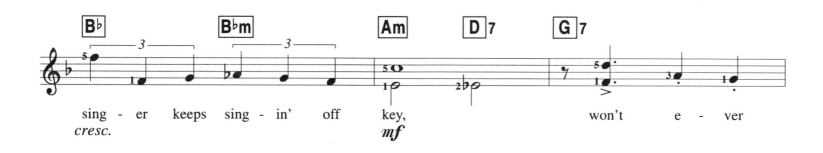

sing - er keeps sing - in' off key, won't e - ver

*cresc.* *mf*

mind if sud - den-ly she \_\_\_\_\_ re - minds you of me! \_\_\_

(he) *f*

flute to guitar

25

IMPROVISATION

*D.C. (Verse 3) al Fine*

# LOVER

Music by Richard Rodgers
Words by Lorenz Hart

**Suggested registration:** accordion
**Rhythm:** jazz waltz
**Tempo:** fast ( ♩ = 168+ )

CHORUS

Lo - ver, _____ when I'm near you, _____ and I
Lo - ver, _____ when we're dan - cing, _____ keep on

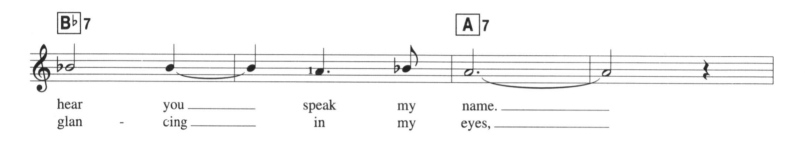

hear you _____ speak my name. _____
glan - cing _____ in my eyes, _____

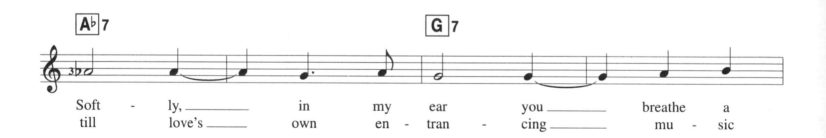

Soft - ly, _____ in my ear you _____ breathe a
till love's _____ own en - tran - cing _____ mu - sic

flame. _____
dies. _____

All of my fu - ture is in you. _____

28

You're e - v'ry plan I de - sign. _____

Pro - mise you'll al - ways con - ti - nue _____ to be
*cresc.*

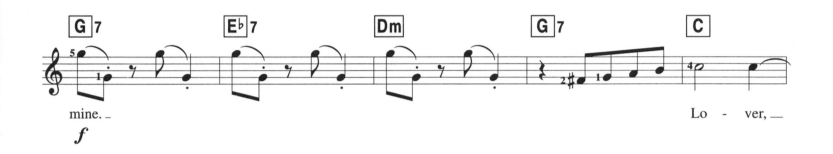

mine. _  
*f*  
Lo - ver, _

_ please be ten - der, _____ when you're ten - der, _____ fears de -

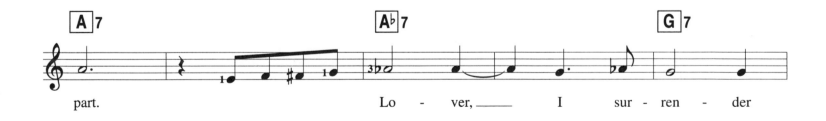

part.  
Lo - ver, _____ I sur - ren - der

to my heart.  
*ff*  
(Fine) accordion to trumpet  
(stop rhythm last time)

29

## IMPROVISATION

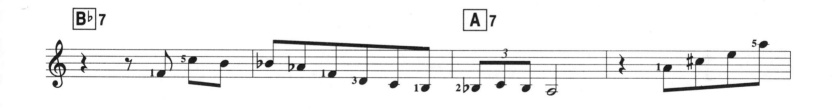

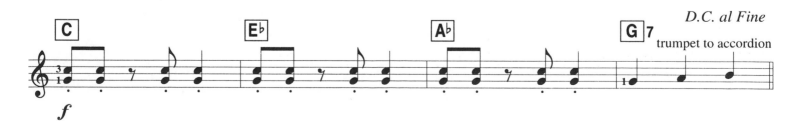

# THE NEARNESS OF YOU

Music by Hoagy Carmichael
Words by Ned Washington

**Suggested registration:** string ensemble
**Rhythm:** swing
**Tempo:** slow ( ♩ = 80 )

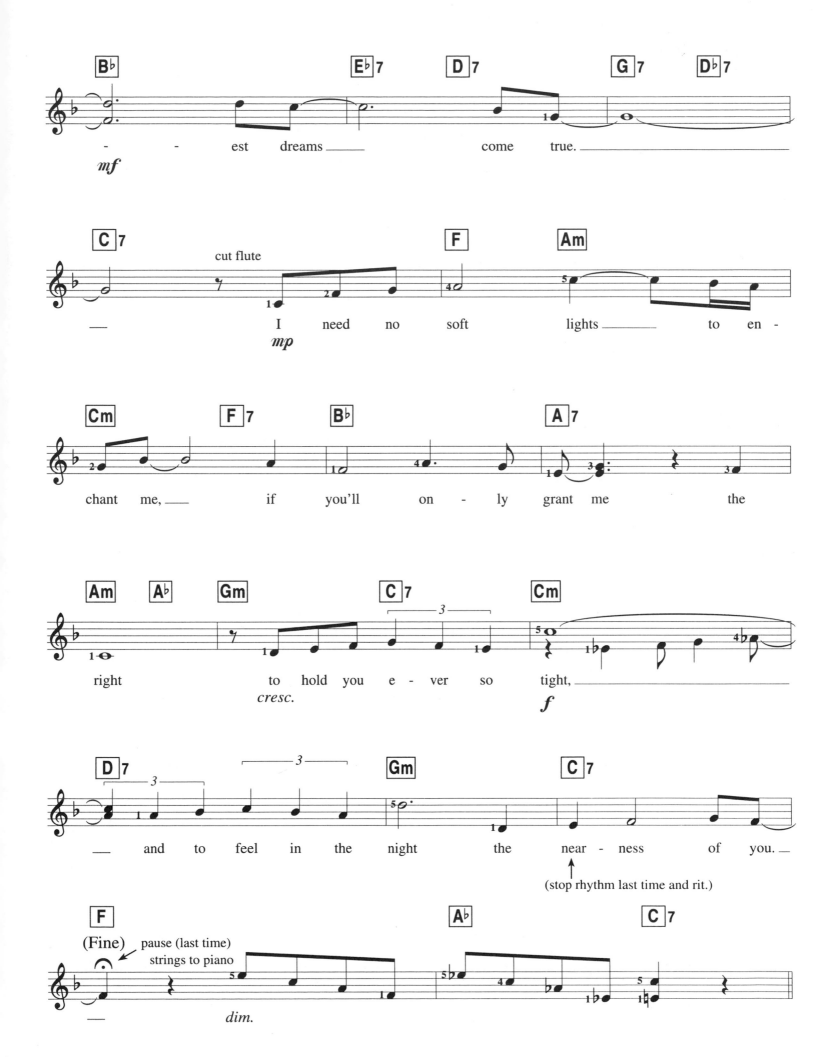

IMPROVISATION

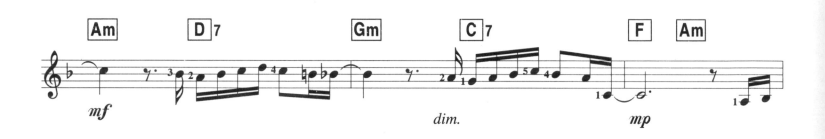

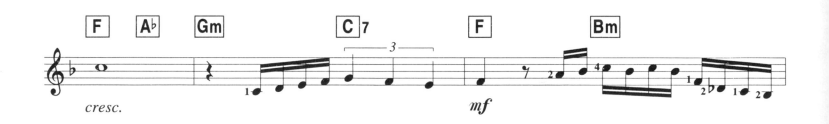

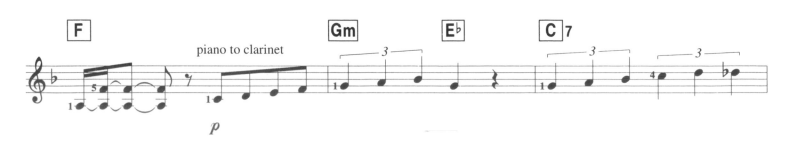

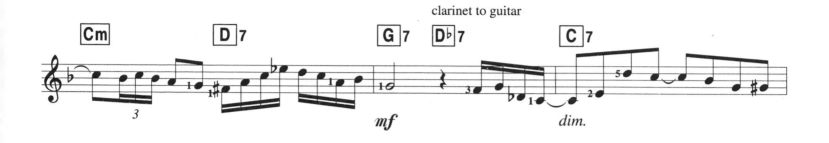

clarinet to guitar

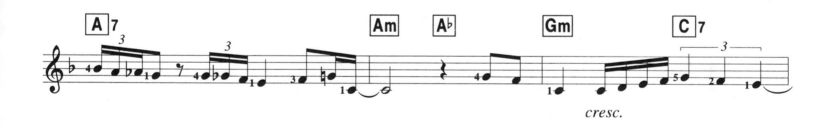

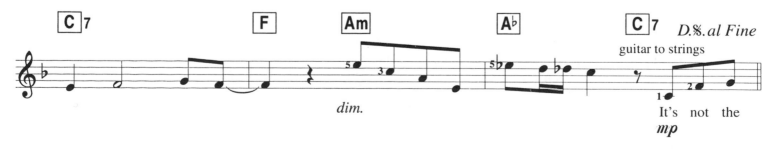

It's not the

# FEVER

Words & Music by John Davenport & Eddie Cooley

**Suggested registration:** brass ensemble

**Rhythm:** swing

**Tempo:** medium ( ♩ = 104 )

* TREMOLO. Roll the two notes, as fast as possible

IMPROVISATION

brass to saxophone

Fe - ver! ___ in the mor - ning, ___ fe - ver all through ___ the night. ___

# CHORD CHARTS (For Left Hand)

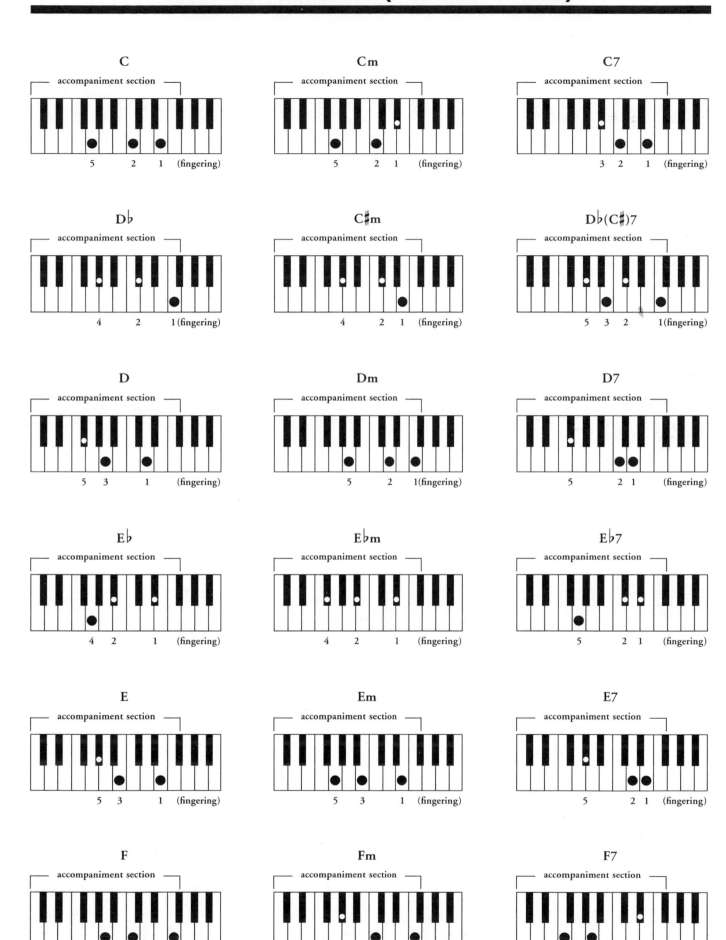

# CHORD CHARTS (For Left Hand)

### Gb(F#)

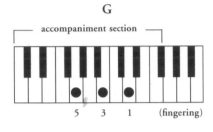

accompaniment section

5  3  1  (fingering)

### F#m

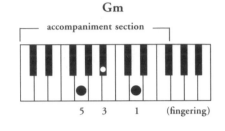

accompaniment section

5  3  1  (fingering)

### Gb(F#)7

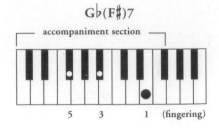

accompaniment section

5  3  1  (fingering)

### G

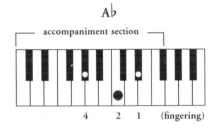

accompaniment section

5  3  1  (fingering)

### Gm

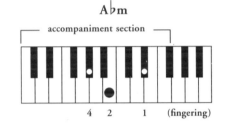

accompaniment section

5  3  1  (fingering)

### G7

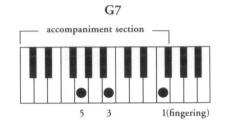

accompaniment section

5  3  1(fingering)

### Ab

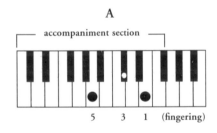

accompaniment section

4  2  1  (fingering)

### Abm

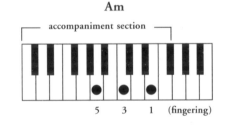

accompaniment section

4  2  1  (fingering)

### Ab7

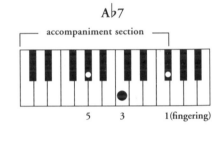

accompaniment section

5  3  1(fingering)

### A

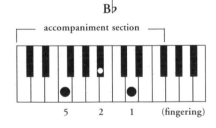

accompaniment section

5  3  1  (fingering)

### Am

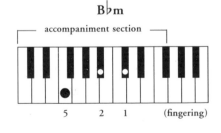

accompaniment section

5  3  1  (fingering)

### A7

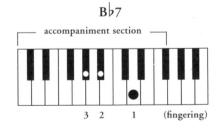

accompaniment section

5  4  2  (fingering)

### Bb

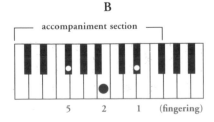

accompaniment section

5  2  1  (fingering)

### Bbm

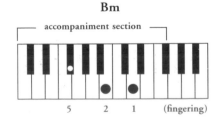

accompaniment section

5  2  1  (fingering)

### Bb7

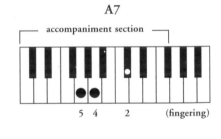

accompaniment section

3  2  1  (fingering)

### B

accompaniment section

5  2  1  (fingering)

### Bm

accompaniment section

5  2  1  (fingering)

### B7

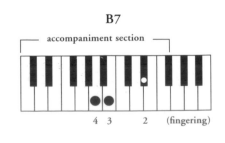

accompaniment section

4  3  2  (fingering)